1979

KENNETH GRAHAME'S

The Wind in the Willows

DRAMATIZED BY

JOSEPH BALDWIN

THE DRAMATIC PUBLISHING COMPANY

CHICAGO

N O T I C E

THE WIND IN THE WILLOWS

A Play in Two Acts

For Seventeen Characters

CHARACTERS

MR. MOLE............... *a small friendly animal*
MR. RAT............. *a water-rat, resident of the river bank*
MR. BADGER.....*venerable and respected resident of the Wild Wood*
MR. TOAD........... *English country gentleman, owner of Toad Hall*
JACK WEASEL.............. *a disreputable fellow*
JEN WEASEL.......................... *his wife*
TOM WEASEL................... *a young weasel*
TILLY WEASEL..........................*his wife*
MRS. OTTER....*a widow residing on the river bank*
PORTLY OTTER..... *very young son of Mrs. Otter*
CHAUFFEUR..........*driver for His Lordship and Her Ladyship*
POLICEMAN.................. *a rural constable*
JAILER.................. *keeper of the dungeon*
PENELOPE...........*the jailer's pretty daughter*
BILL..................... *a locomotive fireman*
ALF........................ *the engine-driver*
WEASEL COOK.......... *employee of the weasels*

EXTRAS: *Offstage voices, such as those of the Prisoners in the dungeon and the Weasels carousing at their banquet.*

3

TIME: *1908.*

PLACE: *The English countryside; in and about Toad Hall, the Wild Wood, and the Castle (dungeon).*

ACT ONE

Scene One

Before the curtain rises there is flute music, as if Pan himself were playing, and as the curtain rises, bird calls are heard. The scene is the neighborhood of Toad Hall. If convenient, there may be a weeping willow tree painted on the backdrop (remembering that on the stage it is outline rather than detail that counts). On the side wings, portions of willows and/or shadows of willows may be painted. If desired there may be a small, real or artificial willow tree. Toad Hall may be merely some impressive chimney-tops above the willow tree painted on flats or a backdrop, or an actual stage setting. A small sign reading:

> TOAD HALL
> PRIVATE PROPERTY
> KEEP OFF
> THIS MEANS YOU!

should be appropriately located. A pointer should indicate the direction to Wild Wood. A few pieces of lawn furniture are desirable, including a bench.

MOLE and RAT enter R, having presumably just landed at Toad's dock.

MOLE

What a wonderful day for a trip on the river! I'm deeply grateful to you, Mr. Rat.

5

RAT

Just call me "Ratty"--all my pals do.

MOLE

Thanks--Ratty.
          (Anxiously)
You're sure Mr. Toad won't mind your bringing me
along?

RAT

Toad mind? He's always glad to show off Toad Hall
and there it is, in all its glory.
          (Gestures largely)

MOLE

          (Leaning his head back)
But I can only see the chimney-tops. And how many
there are! It's a palace! Mr. Toad must be very
rich!

RAT

Rich--and foolish. Always some new fad! Now he's
throwing away his money on cars!

MOLE

          (Worried)
Do you mean he might even lose this beautiful home?

RAT

That's exactly what I mean.
          (Pulls folded newspaper from his pocket
          and gives it to MOLE)
This was in last week's paper.
          (As MOLE takes it)
Go ahead. Read it.

MOLE

          (Reading)

"Toad in hospital--car a total loss!" Oh, my!

RAT

Read on.

MOLE

"Toad demolishes bakery van. Police charges Toad with being an incompetent driver! Magistrate fines Toad!"

RAT
(Extending his hand for the paper)
That's enough.   That tells the story.

MOLE

But shouldn't somebody *do* something?

RAT

Of course.   That's why we're here.   We're meeting Badger.

MOLE
(Impressed)
Mr. Badger of Wild Wood?

RAT

The same.   He knew Toad's father and he's worried, too!   And, if I'm not mistaken, there he comes.

MOLE

There's someone with him.   Following along behind--

RAT
(Peering)
By George, there *is* someone!

MOLE

A very small person.

RAT

Old Badger doesn't know he's there.   Now we'll have
some fun!
                (Moves forward and greets Badger)
Isn't this a long walk for you--all the way from the
Wild Wood?

                    (BADGER enters, carrying a thorny walk-
                    ing-stick.   Trailing BADGER is PORTLY,
                    the young otter, whom BADGER has not
                    seen)

BADGER

Well you may ask, my young friend.   I'm pretty well
winded.
                    (Flops into a chair, breathing hard.   PORT-
                    LY moves over behind Badger's chair)

RAT

Who's this fine, strapping young fellow you have with
you?
                    (Indicates PORTLY, who backs away.
                    BADGER turns, then rises with an excla-
                    mation)

BADGER

Portly Otter!   And I gave you a penny to go home!
                    (PORTLY scuffs his foot and hangs his
                    head.   BADGER turns to the others)
Always tagging along where he isn't wanted!
                    (To PORTLY)
Off with you, my lad.
                    (Turns PORTLY R)
Off.   Off.   Go home!
                    (PORTLY doesn't budge)

RAT

Try him with another penny, Badger.

BADGER
That's encouraging him!
(A struggle within himself)
Well--yes. Here, you little rascal! Now be off!
(Gives the penny to PORTLY, who pockets
it, backs away and then lingers unnoticed)

MOLE
He didn't even say thank you.
(Makes a tsk-tsk sound of disapproval)

BADGER
(Returning to his chair)
Oh, he's completely spoiled. No discipline. Let Mrs.
Otter turn her back and off he goes!
(PORTLY crosses to RAT and touches his
sleeve)

PORTLY
Go with you?

RAT
(Sharply)
Kid, you're a complete nuisance. Now clear out!

(MRS. OTTER enters R)

MRS. OTTER
(Approaching others)
Have you seen----
(Sees PORTLY)
Oh, there you are! Mama was worried!
(Takes his hand and turns to the others)
It's good of you to take Portly about with you so
much.

RAT
Well--actually----

MOLE
(Speaking almost at the same time)
The fact is----

MRS. OTTER
(Puzzled)
What are you talking about?

RAT
We sometimes wonder why the kid doesn't stay
home and play with his friends.

MRS. OTTER
But Portly hasn't any friends.   There aren't any
children his age around.

MOLE
Doesn't he have chores to do around home?

MRS. OTTER
(Stiffly)
I'll see he doesn't bother you in the future.   Come
along, Portly.   Good day, gentlemen.

MOLE
We didn't exactly mean----
            (MRS. OTTER and PORTLY exit)
Oh, dear!

RAT
But we *do* exactly mean.   The kid's a nuisance.

MOLE
He's cute, too--sort of.

BADGER
At least, we don't have to drag him along with us

today.   And now for our interview with Toad.

RAT
(To BADGER)
Are you sure he's home?

BADGER
He said he'd be, when he invited us.
          (Striking the ground with his stick)
I consider it reasonable to expect him there.
          (Offstage R we hear the sound of an auto
          horn: "Poop-poop!")

MOLE
What sound is that?
          (The horn sounds again, and we hear the
          car.   The animals leap upon the bench to
          get a view of the road.   RAT is up first)

RAT
It's roaring down the road!

MOLE
There's a cloud of dust!

RAT
It's a red car!   Coming full speed!

BADGER
Look at the cows gallop!

MOLE
The driver's waving his cap!   Yeah!
          (Waves his own cap)

BADGER
(Peering)

Could it be---- Oh, no!
          (Covers his eyes)

                    RAT
It's Toad!

                    BADGER
Too fast! Reckless!
          (The poop-poop of the horn is heard. All
          turn their heads from R to L as the car
          seemingly dashes past)

                    MOLE
My, it's a grand car!

                    RAT
          (Excited)
He's not slowing for the turn!

                    BADGER
He's looking back and waving----

                    RAT
          (Shouting)
Toad! Look ahead, you idiot!

                    BADGER
Too late!
          (A loud crash off L)

                    MOLE
          (Covering his eyes)
I can't look.

                    BADGER
Ah!

                    RAT
The car's flipping over----

MOLE
(Who has uncovered his eyes)
Look at him sail!

RAT
Into the haystack!

BADGER
Fool's luck!
(Starts for the gate)
Come, let's help the poor lad.

RAT
The car's smashed.

MOLE
(Mournfully)
It was so beautiful.

(BADGER and RAT exit. We hear them
calling to TOAD. After a moment's hes-
itation, MOLE also rushes out. In just a
moment, the group returns, MOLE and
RAT supporting the somewhat breathless
MR. TOAD, BADGER hobbling along behind, anxious about his friend's condition.
TOAD is dressed in cap, goggles, motoring coat, etc., and still grasps the steer-
ing wheel in his hand. A bit of the steer-
ing column remains, to which is attached
a horn with a bulb)

TOAD
(Somewhat dazed, but elated)
Stopped her at last! Hooray!

RAT
(Ruefully, looking off)

That's the last of *that* car.   It's a wonder you lived.

TOAD
The trick is to *leap* at the right moment.   Did you see
me leap?

RAT
I did.

TOAD
The next car I buy, I shall learn, first off, how to
stop her.

BADGER
The *next* car?
            (Muttering)
This is what I feared!

TOAD
Ratty, Badger, my best friends----
            (Pauses, as he sees MOLE clearly)

RAT
            (Quick to make introductions)
Mr. Mole--Mr. Toad.

TOAD
            (Pumping Mole's hand)
Welcome to Toad Hall!

MOLE
            (Much impressed)
Mr. Toad.

TOAD
            (To the group)
How about a cool drink? Such luck you all happened

to turn up just now!

RAT

Don't you remember you invited us to come?

TOAD
(Laughing)
Oh, yes--so I did, so I did!

BADGER

He's dazed.

RAT
(Taking Toad's arm and leading him to a chair)
Sit quiet a bit, Toady.

TOAD

Yes, I wanted you all here. For I've discovered the true purpose of life! Cars!
(MOLE helps RAT seat TOAD)

BADGER
(Staring gloomily toward the road)
You'll never drive this one again. And the money lost!
(Throws up his hands in despair)

TOAD

Pooh! What's money? I shall simply ring up for another car.
(Tugs Rat's sleeve)
Ah, Ratty, this is really living!
(Presses the horn-bulb: "poop-poop!")
The open road, the dusty highway, fields and parks, towns and cities! Here today, gone tomorrow! Travel, change, excitement!

(RAT walks away, shaking his head. TOAD
turns to MOLE)
All of us--to the village this afternoon--for another
car.

BADGER
(Preparing to lecture TOAD)
Now, Toad, you listen to me. Give up this idea of
buying another car. Travel by horse-drawn convey-
ance, as nature intended.

TOAD
Give up! That glorious machine? That poetry of mo-
tion. The only *real* way to travel!
(Rises, and strides about. In his emotion,
he drags the bench downstage and sits astride
it, holding the wheel in his hand)
Here today--in next week tomorrow! Towns skipped,
cities jumped--always a new horizon!
(Squeezes the horn-bulb: "Poop-poop!")
Oh, bliss! Oh, my!

RAT
Toad, stop being silly!

BADGER
The machine nearly killed you just now.

TOAD
Oh, what roads lie before me! What dust clouds
shall spring up behind me! What carts I shall fling
carelessly into the ditch!

RAT
(Staring at TOAD, whose eyes are glazed)
A new craze always takes him like this!

TOAD
(Caught up in his dream)
Poop-poop!
(The others shake their heads and stare at
him with pity)

RAT
(Finger to his lips)
Sh! Wait----

(But a noise off L shatters the quiet. A
sliding and bumping sound, and an angry
exclamation. BADGER rushes to investi-
gate and returns in a moment with JACK
WEASEL, a very disreputable-looking
character. BADGER has him by the ear)

JACK WEASEL
Ouch! Come off it, guvnor! Easy with the ear.
That's attached permanent-like, you know.

BADGER
Come along, or I'll give you a taste of my stick!
(Takes him toward TOAD)
See what was hiding in your carriage house. A sneak-
ing weasel.

TOAD
(Far away)
Poop-poop.
(Becomes aware of this new disturbance)
What? Have we other guests?

BADGER
Like all his kind, uninvited.

JACK WEASEL
(Whining)

I was only taking a bit of a nap in the straw!

                    BADGER
              (Shaking him)
How long have you unlawfully occupied Mr. Toad's
property?

                    JACK WEASEL
Ow, now, it ain't no use being overly hard on a
poor creature what ain't got no home of his own----

                    RAT
True! Tramps and vagabonds, all of them!

                    BADGER
What shall we do with him? Turn him over to the
police?

                    TOAD
Let's not be too harsh! The poor fellow's home-
less. And I've not used the carriage house lately.

                    BADGER
              (Releasing WEASEL)
Aye. Not since your new fad started.

                    TOAD
What's your name, boy?

                    JACK WEASEL
Jack Weasel, sir.
              (Quickly approaches TOAD)
I can tell you're real gentry, sir, and know how
to treat them as is down on their luck----
              (Glances at BADGER)
Not like some as has no hearts.

                    TOAD
              (Chuckling)
Real gentry. Yes! Intelligent fellow.

                    RAT
Encourage one weasel and soon you'll have a whole
pack of them on your hands.

                JACK WEASEL
              (To RAT)
Every chap has a few friends.
              (Pressing his advantage with TOAD)
I was watching when you drove your fine car past,
sir.

                    TOAD
              (Delighted)
You saw me?

                JACK WEASEL
You've a natural talent for driving, sir! Dash and
fire, I say.

                    TOAD
              (To the others)
There!

                JACK WEASEL
And I heard all them other gentlemen said against
you----

                   BADGER
Snooping, eavesdropping!

                JACK WEASEL
I say, you ought buy a bigger car next time. One
with a little more power.

TOAD
(Energetically, rising)
You, good man, may sleep in my carriage house
any time you like!

RAT
That's done it!

JACK WEASEL
And my pals, too? They're adventurers like yourself, sir.

TOAD
(Expansively)
Sure.

JACK WEASEL
(Delighted, cupping hand to mouth and
shouting)
Jen! Tom! Tilly! Out here!

(JEN, TOM and TILLY run on stage and
join JACK. They are young weasels and
rather attractive in a bold and juvenile-
delinquent style)

JACK WEASEL
My wife Jen, my cousin Tom, his wife.
(They curtsy or bow, clustering near as
their names are pronounced)
Mr. Toad!

JEN WEASEL
Not the great Mr. Toad of Toad Hall! The one that
looks so dashing in his motoring clothes?

JACK WEASEL
(Impressively)

The same!

> (JEN clasps her hands and looks at TOAD
> in seeming awe. During this and the fol-
> lowing speeches BADGER, MOLE and RAT
> indicate variously their disgust and exas-
> peration at TOAD for swallowing the crude
> flattery)

TOAD
(Gently pinching her cheek)
Great little wife you've got there, Jack.

TOM WEASEL
Never thought the likes of us would meet the great
Mr. Toad!

TOAD
(Loving it)
Well, now, I'm always glad to make new friends!
(To TILLY)
What's your name, my dear?

TILLY WEASEL
Tilly, sir! Oh, it's just like the fortune teller said,
this is my lucky day! Mr. Toad! Fancy *me* meeting *you* face to face!

TOAD
Well, well, I don't know when I've met such a great
group of young people! Sleep in the carriage house
all you like, my dears.

> (BADGER clasps head in horror, M O L E
> shakes his head, and RAT throws up his
> hands in despair)

JACK WEASEL
(Softly)
We'll do that, count on it.

(The WEASEL group variously register
joy, turning cartwheels or capering with
joy)

TOAD
Now, my good friends, just run up to the kitchen
door and tell Cook you're hungry. Remember,
you're always welcome here.

TOM WEASEL
(As the group is about to leave)
We're powerfully glad to hear you say that, sir, and in
front of witnesses.
(Tips his cap)
Good day to you, sir, and good health. You're a great
driver!
(JEN and TILLY kiss their hands, JACK
and TOM salute TOAD. They exit)

BADGER
(Turning on TOAD)
Toad, you amaze me!

TOAD
(Adjusting his cuffs)
Yes, I'm an amazing fellow.

RAT
You'll have all their pals moving in! The stoats, the
foxes--all the tough characters of the neighborhood.

TOAD
Now, now, let's not make a big thing of a bit of
hospitality! Toad Hall can spare a little refresh-
ment for a few high-spirited young people.
(An expansive gesture)
Now, gentlemen, shall we go up to the Hall for

lunch? Come, Mole. I'll show the way.
> (TOAD takes Mole's arm)

After lunch, off to adventure and the open road!
> (TOAD and MOLE start to exit. RAT
> throws up his hands in disgust but BADGER
> restrains him)

BADGER
> (Holding up his stick)

Stop! I'm sorry, Toad, but you force me to do this.
It's for your own good.
> (To MOLE and RAT)

Mole, Rat, take that ridiculous outfit off him, at
once.
> (MOLE and RAT seize TOAD and throw
> him down, kicking and screaming. They
> remove his goggles, motoring coat, hat
> and gloves and stand him up again, some-
> what subdued)

TOAD
Now look here, Badger----

RAT
Now you are no longer Toad, the Terror of the
Highway.
> (TOAD giggles feebly, and looks from
> one to the other in mute appeal)

BADGER
You knew it must come to this sooner or later. You've
paid no attention to the police; you've gone on squander-
ing the money your father left you----

RAT
You've spent days and nights in the hospital----

BADGER
That, too. And you're getting the decent animals of

the district a bad name with your reckless driving.

                    TOAD
            (Wheedling)
My dear old Badger, you've always known my adventurous, free spirit . . .
            (He quails before Badger's imperious glare)

                    BADGER
            (To MOLE and RAT)
Gentlemen, if you will excuse us for a moment?
            (MOLE and RAT retire to a corner of the
            stage. As BADGER lectures TOAD they
            listen, leaning toward BADGER and TOAD,
            sometimes cupping an ear to hear better.
            Whenever attention turns their way, they
            pretend not to be listening)
Step this way, Toad. Now! Independence is all very
well. But we animals never allow our friends to
make fools of themselves----

                    MOLE
Beyond a certain limit.
            (BADGER glares at MOLE, and MOLE
            retires to the other side of RAT)

                    BADGER
            (To TOAD)
--and that limit you've reached! Now, you're a good
fellow in many respects, and I don't want to be too
hard on you. I'll make one more effort to bring you
to reason. You are now going to hear some facts
about yourself.

                    TOAD
            (Giggling nervously)
Facts? About me?

BADGER

First, consider your ancestors! None of them have
ever been arrested before! But you----

TOAD

Only--once--or twice----

BADGER

Five times before the Magistrate! That time you hit
the tradesman's cart. What if you'd hit *him?* Think,
Toad. He has six children!
    (Holds up six fingers)
Think of the six orphaned children of that honest
tradesman.
    (TOAD turns away, sobbing)
And what if, next time, you not only smash your car,
but yourself? Think, Toad. Think of your friends,
Rat, and Mole, and me, all in black, bringing wreaths
of flowers--to your *funeral.*
    (TOAD drops to his knees)

TOAD

Enough! Mercy!

BADGER

Do you promise never to buy another car?

TOAD

I promise. I'll promise anything! Only don't talk
about the six orphaned children--and my funeral--I
can't bear it!

BADGER

Then give me your checkbook to keep for a while, so
you won't be tempted.

TOAD
(Giving checkbook to BADGER)

Here.
(Wipes his eyes)

BADGER
(Helping TOAD to a chair)

There. Dry your eyes. You'll thank me for this, some day.
(To RAT and MOLE)

You may approach, gentlemen.
(RAT and MOLE come downstage)

My friends, I am pleased to inform you that Toad has seen the error of his ways. He has given up cars forever. I have his solemn promise.

MOLE
Good news!
(Shakes Toad's hand)

BADGER
Of course, Toad's weak yet, and we shall have to stay with him in the Hall and guard him against backsliding.

RAT
It's all for your own good, Toady, you know!

MOLE
We'll take care of everything for you.

RAT
No more brawls with the police.

MOLE
And no more weeks in hospital!

(Toad's sorrowful face begins to have a wicked look. Only RAT observes this. He shoves his hands into his pockets and glares at TOAD)

BADGER

The good work begins. Toad, I want you to solemnly repeat, before your friends here, what you said to me just now. First, you're truly sorry for the wrong you've done, and you see the folly of it.

TOAD

I'm truly sorry----
                    (A pause. Then TOAD leaps from his chair
                    and goes for his driving clothes)
No! I'm *not* sorry!
                    (Claps his motoring cap onto his head)
And it wasn't folly. It was simply glorious!
                    (Struggles into the greatcoat)

BADGER

What! You backsliding animal, didn't you tell me, just now----

TOAD

                    (Pulling on the gauntleted gloves)
Oh, yes, yes, just *now*. I'd have said anything *then*. You were so eloquent, dear Badger, and put all your points so frightfully well--you really took advantage of me!

RAT

                    (To MOLE)
What did I tell you?

TOAD

But I've been thinking it over--and I've also remembered what my Weasel friends said. *They* like me. They think I cut a very dashing figure in my motoring clothes! And they think I drive very well.

                    RAT
Can't you see through them, Toad?

                    TOAD
I'm beginning to see who my *real* friends are. Weasels! I propose to order another red motor car immediately.

                    BADGER
          (Grimly)
Rat. Mole. We must save him from himself. Get ready.
          (MOLE and RAT move toward TOAD,
          meaning to grab him. TOAD watches
          them, a crafty look on his face)

                    TOAD
          (Pretending to go into a daze)
Poop--Poop! Poop--Poop!
          (Swings a bench around and sits astride
          it)
The red limousine is mine! Poop-poop!

                    RAT
          (Awed)
He's having an attack.

                    TOAD
          (Eyes glazed)
I'm Toad! King of the Road! Poop--poop!
          (Sways and clutches the wheel as he pan-
          tomimes driving furiously)

MOLE
Poor animal, he doesn't even know we're here!

TOAD
R-r-roar! Adventure! Excitement! The open road!
(BADGER goes to TOAD and shakes him)

BADGER
Toad? Toad?
(Toad's only reply is a weak "Poop--poop!"
His eyes glaze over, his body stiffens)
Mole, go wet your handkerchief in the river.
(MOLE hastens off R)

RAT
He's growing weaker. It's a real attack.

BADGER
We don't dare move him, in this condition.

(MOLE rushes in, with a wet handkerchief)

BADGER
Ah, Mole. Good. Apply it to his forehead--gently.
Poor creature!
(MOLE does so)

BADGER
We must watch over the poor delirious fellow.   He
might harm himself if we left him alone.

RAT
(Passing hand over Toad's eyes)
He's unconscious.

MOLE
(Meekly)
Do you think he'll be well in time for tea?

BADGER
(Scornfully)
Tea! At a time like this!

(MRS. OTTER enters in a rush)

MRS. OTTER
Thank heaven you're still here!

BADGER
(Pointing to TOAD)
Quiet!
(Puts finger on lip)

MRS. OTTER
(Without heeding)
Did Portly come back?

BADGER
The last time I saw him, he was with you.

RAT
I thought you were taking him home.

MRS. OTTER
I stopped to buy him some books----

MOLE
A good idea. A few adventure stories----

MRS. OTTER
(Glowering)
Improving books. I thought I'd teach him to read--

only he didn't seem much interested.

RAT

What happened?

MRS. OTTER

Nothing happened. I was glancing through the books
to be sure they'd be right for him and then----

MOLE
(Eagerly)
And then?

MRS. OTTER

Portly was gone. He didn't go home, either!

MOLE

Maybe he's at one of the neighbors'.

MRS. OTTER

Portly never goes there. It's you fellows he thought
so much of. So I came on to ask if you'd seen
him.

BADGER

No--but I'm sure nothing's happened to a fine, sen-
sible lad like Portly.

MOLE
(Dubiously)
He's not very old.

RAT

Do you suppose he could have run off to the Wild
Wood?

MRS. OTTER
(Anguished)

Oh, not the Wild Wood!

MOLE
(Horrified)
Dark, and deep, and dangerous! He'd never risk go-
ing there!

BADGER
(Sharply)
Hush, Mole. It's not so dangerous as all that. I
live there myself--well, in the more open part.
(To MRS. OTTER)
Never fear, we'll find Portly. Come on, Mole. Rat,
you stay here and watch over Toad.

RAT
Very well.

BADGER
Sharply, mind?

RAT
Certainly, you can depend on me.

(BADGER, MRS. OTTER, and MOLE exit
through the gate and go down the road, L.
RAT sits anxiously watching. TOAD sits
up and speaks in a hoarse, broken voice)

TOAD
Rat? Rat? Is it you, my old friend?

RAT
Righto. Toad! Feeling better?

TOAD
Oh, yes. As much as I'm likely to--now.

RAT

Good! Do you want to try to sit up for a while?

TOAD

Dear, kind Rat! How little you realize!
        (Sorrowfully)
But don't trouble about me. I hate being a burden
to my friends, and I don't expect to be one much
longer.

RAT

        (Heartily)
Well, you've been a fine bother to us all, and I'm
glad to hear it's going to stop.

TOAD

I shan't trouble you further--oh--ulp!
        (Falls back)

RAT

Toad!
        (Shakes him)
Toad! What is it!

TOAD

        (Weakly)
Don't trouble about me . . .

RAT

        (Worried)
Can I do something for you?

TOAD

If you'd be so kind--my last request--step 'round
to the village and fetch the doctor--quickly.

RAT

The doctor! What for?

TOAD

Surely you've known of my injuries lately? My times in hospital?

RAT

Yes--yes----

TOAD

And that scuffle just now--I blame no one--but in my serious condition----

RAT
(Suspicious)

Toad! Is this pretense?

TOAD

Call it what you will. Why *should* you trouble? Perhaps tomorrow--you may be saying to yourself-- "Oh, if only I had listened to him! If only I'd done something sooner!"
(Falls back, exhausted)

RAT

Toad! I'm going.
(On way to gate)

I'll fetch the doctor instantly. Do you hear, dear old Toad?

TOAD

Faithful Rat! Yes, I hear. And--I hate to give you additional trouble, but would you mind also asking the lawyer to step 'round?

RAT
(Aghast)

The *lawyer!* Whatever for?

TOAD

To make out my will, dear old friend.
          (Faintly)
Haste! Time grows short.

RAT

          (Wiping his eyes)
Oh, Toad, I can't bear it. How we'll miss you!
          (Dashes out at the gate. TOAD waits a bit,
          then looks about, craftily, and springs up)

TOAD

Fell for it! I thought he would!
          (Quickly adjusting his clothes)
Now! Once again Toad will be King of the Road!
          (Pauses)
But how to get to the village?

          (JACK WEASEL appears from off L)

JACK WEASEL

Sst! Guvnor! Over here.

TOAD

          (Going to him)
Weasel, my dear friend!

JACK WEASEL

I hung about in case you needed help. I've got a
bicycle hid out back. How about a lift to the village?

TOAD

Capital, my dear fellow! A true friend--that's
what you are!

JACK WEASEL

Hey, Jen--quick with the bike!

(JEN wheels on a bicycle)

JACK WEASEL

Let's hop it, sir! We can take turns riding the bike.
I know where there's a lovely new limousine in the
village.   A purple one.

TOAD
            (Ecstatic)
Purple!

JACK WEASEL

Hurry, before that bunch of killjoys comes back!
            (Gleefully)
It's downhill most of the way.

TOAD

Righto!
            (Joyfully they go off L: "Poop--poop!")

            (In just a moment, BADGER, MOLE, and
            MRS. OTTER enter the gate, from the road)

BADGER
            (Talking over his shoulder)
He's not down that way.
            (Turns)
Rat, we're going on down the road----
            (Sees no one is present)
Rat?
            (The others come in and stare at the empty
            stage)
Now where are they?

            (RAT rushes in at the gate, talking as he
            comes)

RAT

Toad! I couldn't find either your doctor or your lawyer.
(Sees the empty chair)
What? Gone?

BADGER

Gone.

RAT

Gone?

BADGER

(Grimly)
How did he fool you?

RAT

He said he way dying. He begged me to go for his doctor. And for his lawyer--to make his will.
(MOLE snickers, and is frowned into silence. RAT is crestfallen)
He did it awfully well.

BADGER

He did *you* awfully well. However, talking won't mend matters. We must think what to do!

RAT

He *may* come back for his checkbook. He can't buy much without it.

MOLE

Clever Rat!

RAT

Oh, I don't miss much.

        (MOLE giggles, and BADGER frowns at him)

BADGER

Here's the plan. Mrs. Otter and I will search the
Wild Wood for Portly. Mole, you hotfoot it down the
high road to the village. Alert the police. Tell them
about Portly's being lost and also that it's urgent
they find Toad before there's more harm done.

        (MOLE goes to the gate)

Rat, you stay here. If Toad comes home before we
get back, don't let him trick you again.

RAT

        (Grimly)

I'll "doctor" him! He'll need to write his will for
sure when I'm through with him!

MOLE

        (At gate)

How dreadful! Portly and Toad both--missing their
tea.

BADGER

Mole, I insist--*try* to be serious!

        (MOLE, abashed, hurries on out the gate.
        BADGER offers MRS. OTTER his arm)

Come along, Mrs. Otter. Keep your courage up.

MRS. OTTER

It's just he was such a lonely child--if I'd taken better care of him----

        (Wipes eyes. BADGER a..d MRS. OTTER
        exit. R A T picks up the steering wheel
        Toad has left behind, gives the horn-bulb
        a squeeze: "Poop--poop!" Angrily tosses
        it aside)

RAT

Hunting a doctor and a lawyer! What a sucker!
(Sits glowering as he begins his vigil)

CURTAIN

ACT ONE

Scene Two

TOAD appears before the curtain, along
with JACK WEASEL, pushing the bicycle.

TOAD
(Singing)
O was there ever a Toad so clever
     As Toad of Toad Hall?
He's foxed his friends to gain his ends,
     O he's the slyest of all!
(To JACK WEASEL)
A poem. And now to buy the purple limousine, and
then----
(Winks)
Poop-poop! Want to come along?

JACK WEASEL
Well, now, I'd like to, sir, but I've got to take this
here bicycle back to where Jen borrowed it----

TOAD
(Winking and nudging JACK WEASEL)
Borrowed, did you say?

JACK WEASEL

In a manner of speaking, sir.
          (Grins, appreciating the joke)

TOAD

I'll bet!
          (Off on another tack)
Well, the sooner I get my purple limousine, the
sooner I can start looking.

JACK WEASEL

Looking for what, sir?

TOAD

For young Portly, of course.   You knew he's lost?

JACK WEASEL
          (Puzzled)
Sure, guvnor.   Only what'll you do with him if you
find him?

TOAD
          (Surprised at the question)
Take him back to his mother, of course.   What
else?

JACK WEASEL
          (Has an idea)
Of course--just like you say--only----

TOAD

Only what?

JACK WEASEL

Only some folks might think a growing kid like
that'd be better off making himself useful.

                    TOAD
            (Incredulous)
Young Portly? What could he do?

                  JACK WEASEL
Oh, the kid's getting bigger all the time. He could
be trained to work. Might not be a bad idea at all
--not--at--all--bad.
            (JACK WEASEL exits in the opposite direc-
            tion)

                    TOAD
            (Looking after him a moment, puzzled)
Now what did that mean?
            (Brushes off the thought)
Oh, well----
            (Begins to sing)

O was there ever a creature so clever
      As the celebrated Toad?
It's out the window, as only he kin-do,
      And sing hey for the open road!
            (A caper, and he's off)

            (The curtains part, revealing a magnificent
            canary yellow limousine, with CHAUFFEUR.
            /NOTE: This is a two-dimensional cut-out
            scenery piece./ TOAD enters)

                    TOAD
O was there ever a creature so clever----
            (Stops upon seeing the magnificent vehicle,
            and whistles. Walks about it, appreciative-
            ly)
Well! Well, well, well. What--have--we--here!

                  CHAUFFEUR
A limousine, sir. Have you never seen a fine car?

TOAD

Seen a fine car? I should jolly well hope so. They're my life! But *this* one! There's something very special about it!

CHAUFFEUR

Quite.

TOAD

(Rubbing his hands and beaming)

Oh! She's sleek and powerful!

(As he moves around the car, his eyes are growing larger, and his heart is thumping)

CHAUFFEUR

Very expensive, too.

TOAD

I don't care! I must have it! Name your price! I'll just make out a check----

(Reaches in all his pockets, ends up dismayed and empty-handed)

Clever Badger.

CHAUFFEUR

Sorry, sir. The limousine's not for sale.

TOAD

No? And--unfortunately, I seem to have mislaid my checkbook. Ha! Ha! Not yours, you say?

CHAUFFEUR

No, sir. I drive for his Lordship and her Ladyship. They're inside the shop, having tea.

TOAD

Must be fun, sitting there, in such a lovely limousine!

CHAUFFEUR

Bit of a bore, actually.

TOAD

Then--why not let me mind it for you?

CHAUFFEUR

You, sir?

TOAD

Yes, I.

CHAUFFEUR

But why would you want to do that, sir?

TOAD

Perhaps--only to do you a favor.

CHAUFFEUR

But how do I know you're the reliable sort, sir?

TOAD

(Fishing in his pocket and producing a card)
My card.

CHAUFFEUR

(Reading)
"Toad. Of Toad Hall"?

TOAD

The same. And here's a picture of Toad Hall.
(Shows it)

CHAUFFEUR

Oh, sir, I see you're definitely of the upper crust, sir, but it's my duty to stay with the car.

TOAD
(Taking a new tack)
Pity. Hot work, isn't it, sitting out here in the sun?

CHAUFFEUR
Beastly hot, sir.

TOAD
Wouldn't a cool drink be nice?

CHAUFFEUR
Oh, sir, don't tempt me with ideas of that sort.
(Breaks down, losing all his starch and
dignity)
Most of all, don't tempt me with money, sir. I try
to do my duty, but money tempts me. Pray keep it
in your pocket, sir.

TOAD
Perhaps--this?
(TOAD produces a coin, and the CHAUF-
FEUR leaps out of the car. TOAD as nimbly
leaps in)

CHAUFFEUR
Mind, if you see his Lordship or her Ladyship coming out of the Tea Shop, just give the horn-bulb a
bit of a squeeze to signal me, and then--off you go!
Agreed?

TOAD
Agreed.

CHAUFFEUR
Cheer-oh.

TOAD
Cheer-oh.

(The CHAUFFEUR departs)

Lovely! Just to sit here. Can't be any harm in just sitting here.

(Takes the wheel in his hands)

As long as I'm sitting here, can't be any harm in just putting my hands on the wheel. What could be more natural?

(MOLE comes in, running, and pauses to catch his breath. He starts back at the sight of TOAD)

MOLE

Toad, you, here!

TOAD

(Turning)

Who else?

MOLE

I'm hunting Portly.

TOAD

I thought you wanted to get rid of him.

MOLE

Don't remind me! If we'd been kinder to Portly, he wouldn't have run away. And on top of all our worry about little Portly, I see you've gone and bought a limousine.

TOAD

Now there you wrong me, Mole. It's not mine. I'm only minding the car for a friend.

MOLE

A likely story!

TOAD

Then get in and wait with me until the driver returns.
You'll see.

MOLE

I'll get in the car, but only to watch over you until
help comes.

TOAD

Mole, you wound me. What harm is there just to *sit*
in the limousine, to *feel* the limousine, to *smell* it,
to *imagine* it going?

MOLE

To imagine it going gives me the shudders.

TOAD
(Fooling with knobs and levers)
I wonder what this little lever does?

MOLE

Toad!

TOAD

I wonder if it *starts* easily?
(Moves a lever, and we hear the sound of
the motor)

MOLE

Toad! It *has* started.

TOAD
(Chuckling)
So it has! Ha! Ha! So it has!
(Motor sounds faster)

MOLE

Toad, this is wrong!

TOAD

Mm, yes. Ha! Ha! Now for a burst of speed!

MOLE

Toad, it's stealing!

TOAD

Nonsense. I'm still watching the car. *Now*, I'm
watching it move.
          (Elated)
And *how* it moves!

MOLE
          (A wail of terror)
Toad--I feel--dizzy----

TOAD

And I feel like singing!
          (Sings)

The world has held great Heroes,
          As history-books have showed,
But never a name to go down to fame
          Compared with that of Toad!

MOLE

Toad! That's conceited!

TOAD

Ha! Ha! Yes, isn't it!
          (Sings)

The animals sat in the Ark and cried,
          Their tears in torrents flowed.
Who was it said, "There's land ahead"?
          Encouraging Mr. Toad!

MOLE
          (Pointing ahead)

Someone's standing in the middle of the highway!

TOAD
(Sings)

The Army all saluted
As they marched along the road.
Was it the King? Or Kitchener?
No. It was Mr. Toad!

MOLE
It's a policeman. Stop, Toad.

TOAD
Only a country constable. I'll just slow down and speak with the honest fellow. Just watch me handle him.
(Motor noise: slow)
Smooth stop, Moley.
(Dismounts and calls out)
My good man, kindly explain why you are blocking the public highway with your person?
(He takes off one glove and slaps it in his hand in a cavalier fashion)

(The POLICEMAN steps in)

POLICEMAN
Halt.

TOAD
See here, my good man. Do you realize to whom you are speaking?

POLICEMAN
Mr. Toad of Toad Hall, sir, wot's just made off with his Lordship's limousine.

TOAD
Made off with his Lordship's limousine! Why, why

--how did you find out so soon?
> (Catches himself)

I mean--you insulting fellow--I am Toad of Toad Hall. What gave you the ridiculous idea I stole his Lordship's limousine? I'll have your badge for this!

POLICEMAN
His Lordship's chauffeur, sir. He give me the notion.

TOAD
> (Stricken)

His chauffeur?

POLICEMAN
Recognized you for the desperate character you be, sir, and nipped off straight to the police station.

TOAD
The traitor! And after the tip I gave him!

POLICEMAN
Hardly payment for the limousine, sir.

TOAD
> (To MOLE)

Speak up, Mole! Are you going to let this stupid cop abuse me on the public highway?

POLICEMAN
> (Writing in notebook)

Driving at desperate speed to the public danger. The judge'll give you three years for that.

MOLE
I advise speaking politely to the officer.

TOAD
Officer? This booby?

MOLE

Careful, Toad----

POLICEMAN

Insulting an officer. Old Judge Hangworthy usually sentences fifteen years for that.

TOAD

I dare him to!

POLICEMAN

(Going over the figures in his notebook)
It adds up to a nice long term, sir.
(Takes TOAD by the collar)
Come along now, sir.

TOAD

Mole! Are you going to let this fellow haul me
away?

POLICEMAN

Interfering with an officer of the law is a serious
offense.
(To MOLE)
Care to join us, sir?

MOLE

Another time. Thanks. Toad, want me to call your
lawyer?

TOAD

I forbid it! I'll handle this myself.

POLICEMAN

(Dragging TOAD off)
The prison food is excellent.

TOAD

I'll refuse to eat!

(He is gone, shouting and protesting. MOLE
leans against the limousine, using his handkerchief)

MOLE

Farewell, Toad. Good-by, my dear old friend! Gone
--perhaps forever--and little Portly, too!
(He flutters the handkerchief at the depart-
ing Toad, then breaks down weeping in
earnest)

CURTAIN

ACT ONE

Scene Three

The scene is played in two areas. Area
One is the dungeon of an ancient castle. The
effect is achieved by area lighting and offstage sounds.   The spot reveals an area
containing a crude table, and two chairs or
stools and a rough cot. There is straw on
the floor. Offstage sounds consist of the
clanking of chains, the hoots and jeers of
other prisoners, the jingling of the jailer's
keys and the clang of a heavy iron door.
There may be, if desired, the measured
tread of a watchman making his rounds, the
jingling of his keys and the flicker of his
lantern.   Area Two need only consist of a
stool for the use of Mole in writing his
letter.

Offstage someone is being dragged along the corridor to the cell, accompanied by the hoots and jeers of the other prisoners. It is the unfortunate MR. TOAD, flanked by the POLICEMAN and the JAILER.

VOICES
(Offstage)

Look at him struggle! Yeow! Step on the gas, Toad! Where's your fancy limousine now, yer 'ighness? Oooh, the poor critter--he's crying!

JAILER
(Offstage, bawling)

Quiet down, the lot of you!

VOICES
(Offstage)

Aww-rr!

(But they quiet down)

(The JAILER opens the door offstage, which moves with much jangling and clanking. He and the POLICEMAN hustle TOAD into the cell)

TOAD
(Trying to thrust the policeman away)

You can't do this to me, I tell you!

POLICEMAN

Can't I?

(Sends TOAD sprawling on the floor. He turns to the JAILER)

He's all yours now, Jailer, for twenty years. The Magistrate made it a nice round figure.

(The POLICEMAN and the JAILER step

outside the cell and we hear the door clang
shut offstage)

TOAD
(Rising on his hands and shouting after them)
I demand a fair trial!

POLICEMAN
You've had one, sir.

TOAD
(Springing to his feet)
Let me out! Let me out!

JAILER
My business is keeping in, not letting out.
(We hear the jingle of keys as the door is
locked)

TOAD
I demand the right to see my lawyer!

VOICES
Aaw! 'is 'ighness demands his lawyers.

TOAD
(Strongly)
I tell you! I am Toad of Toad Hall, a gentleman!

VOICES
(Offstage)
Hear that? He's a gentleman!
That's nothing--I was a duke!
(Falsetto) And I was a duchess!
Ha! Ha! Ha!
Ha! Ha! Ha!
(Frightened by the weird voices, TOAD

falls sobbing on his wretched cot)

VOICES
Aaw! I do believe he's bawling!
Can't hev that nohaow!
Sing 'im a song, mates.
Cheer up 'is lordship!
>(The VOICES sing the following rhyme, in-
>terspersed with whistles and catcalls)

The motor car went Poop-Poop-Poop
>As it raced along the road.
Who was it steered it straight to jail?
>Ingenious Mr. Toad!

JAILER
>(Bellowing in tones of authority)
Quiet, you! Quiet, I say!
>(There is the jingle of his keys and the clang
>of the heavy door)

>(The JAILER enters and places a plate of
>food on Toad's table)

JAILER
>(Shaking Toad's shoulder)
Here, now. Perk up and eat something hot. It'll all
seem better.
>(TOAD looks up, wipes away his tears, and
>tries to look disdainful)

TOAD
What is that horrid smell?

JAILER
Good hearty cabbage and potatoes.

TOAD
I don't like cabbage.

JAILER

It's that or nothing.

TOAD

So be it; nothing, then!

JAILER

As you wish, sir. But let me inform you that you'll grow perishing thin.

> (Removes the food and exits. There is the clanging of the great iron gate and jingle of keys)

VOICES

(Offstage)

Hear that? The gentleman won't eat!
What's the matter? Don't he like our cuisine?
What a pity! No pheasant under glass.
Ha! Ha! Ha! Ha! Ha!

> (TOAD, frightened by the voices, and wrung with remorse, stumbles over to the wall and kneels in a pile of straw and wails)

TOAD

All is lost! This is the end of everything!

> (He buries his head in his hands and weeps)

> (Unseen by TOAD, PENELOPE, the jailer's pretty daughter, enters with a tray of hot buttered toast and tea, and quietly sets it on the table. She sits on one of the stools and observes TOAD with pity and curiosity)

TOAD

(Lifting his head to mourn aloud)

Yes, this is the end! At least it's the end of Toad. The rich and hospitable Toad, the Toad so free and debonair!

(His sobs choke him, and his head is down
again.   PENELOPE quietly pours herself
a cup of tea and then begins to munch on a
piece of toast.   TOAD recovers his voice)
Stupid animal that I was! I see it now--I let the
Weasels lead me astray, by flattering me. Oh, wise
old Badger! Why didn't I listen to you?

PENELOPE
(Quietly)
Do you always talk to yourself like that?

TOAD
(Startled)
I beg your pardon. I didn't know anyone was listen-
ing, much less a lady.

PENELOPE
I am the Jailer's daughter, Penelope. I came straight-
way here when Father said you wouldn't eat. I brought
along some of my own tea and toast.

TOAD
You are kind, my dear young lady. But it is useless
to try to console me!

PENELOPE
Now cheer up, Toad. Sit up and try to eat a bit.
(TOAD pauses, obviously tempted by the
odor of the warm buttered toast. But he
maintains his resolution)

TOAD
I have given the word of an English gentleman I will
touch no food. . . . Is the tea hot?
(The hungry TOAD finds himself drawing
nearer to the food)

PENELOPE
Very hot. I'm sure you're too polite to cause a lady
to have tea alone? Just for the sake of good manners,
do sit and have a bite.

TOAD
Well----
      (Stiffens)
No!
      (Weakens)
Is there marmalade?

PENELOPE
Heaps.
      (Hunger wins out over pride, and TOAD sits
      on the other stool and begins devouring toast
      and marmalade, washing the bites down with
      gulps of tea)
Now, that's better! I knew we should get on well.
      (Hands him freshly buttered toast)
Tell me about Toad Hall.

TOAD
      (Regaining pride)
Toad Hall is a self-contained gentleman's residence,
dating in part from the fourteenth century.

PENELOPE
Bless you! I don't want to *rent* it. Tell me something
real about it.

TOAD
      (Staring into the distance)
Oh, if only you could see it! The boathouse, the fish-
pond, the old walled kitchen garden, the banqueting
hall, where I and the other animals gathered to feast,
sing songs, and tell stories. Oh, if only I were there
now!

PENELOPE
Perhaps you shall be soon, Mr. Toad. More tea?

(The lights dim down on the jail area and
a spot comes up on MOLE. He is seated
on a stool and is writing a letter. His head
is bandaged and his arm is in a sling)

MOLE
(Reciting as he writes)
Dear friend Toad, it hurts me to write you this letter
for I have bad news. There is still no news of Portly
and we fear his mother may not live long unless he
is found. And there is more bad news. When we
tried to return to Toad Hall we were set upon by
twenty weasels. I was beaten up and thrown out, as
were all your friends. And we don't really know what
to do. As of now the weasels are in full possession
of Toad Hall!

(The spotlight goes out on MOLE and the
lights come back up on Toad's cell. TOAD
sits with bowed head and groans sorrowful-
ly)

TOAD
(To himself)
It's so lonely here. One gray gloomy day after an-
other.

(Then PENELOPE appears, opens the cell
door, and plumps a fine pudding down before
him. TOAD leaps up, smiling)

TOAD
Penelope again. You're always my benefactress.
(Eagerly)

What did you bring this time?

PENELOPE
A pudding. A real plum pudding. And punch.

TOAD
You are so kind.

PENELOPE
(Reaching into her apron pocket to bring
out a letter)
Also a letter. It's from your friend Mole.

TOAD
From dear old Mole? I don't deserve it.
(He reads)
No! No! No!

PENELOPE
What's happened?

TOAD
Here----
(He hands her the letter. Rages)
If only I could be there, to protect my home, and
join the search for that dear child!
(Leans on the table, weeping)
In prison! Oh, my dear friends! Oh, my folly!

PENELOPE
(Going to TOAD)
Courage, now. Eat your pudding.
(TOAD straightens up and obeys her)

TOAD
(Eating)
Excellent pudding. Rare punch.

PENELOPE

Toad----

TOAD

Yes?

PENELOPE

Just listen, please. I have an aunt who is a washer-woman.

TOAD
(Patting her hand)
There, there. Never mind. I have several aunts who ought to be washerwomen.

PENELOPE

She does the washing for all the prisoners in this castle, and she's in and out so much the guards never notice her. All doors are open to her.

TOAD

Lucky!

PENELOPE

You could dress in her bonnet and apron and skirt, and easily walk out of here. You're very alike in many respects--particularly about the figure.

TOAD
(Huffily)
We're *not*. I have a very elegant figure--for what I am.

PENELOPE

So has my aunt, for what *she* is. But have it your own way, you proud, ungrateful animal!

TOAD

You are a good, kind, clever girl. And I am indeed
a proud and stupid toad. Introduce me to your wor-
thy aunt, if you will be so kind. Perhaps she and I
can come to an agreement. That is, if she won't
expect payment until I get home.

PENELOPE
(Leaping up)

Oh, good! My beloved aunt understands all that. She
is in the kitchen having tea. I have her laundry basket outside, with an extra set of her clothes. Now,
off with your coat and weskit, and throw them on the
bed.

> (PENELOPE runs out and gets the basket,
> while TOAD obeys her commands)

> (PENELOPE returns, and begins putting
> the washerwoman costume on TOAD over
> his soft shirt and trousers)

PENELOPE

First, the cotton print gown. Over your head it goes!
And now to hook it up the back.

TOAD
(Spreading the skirt)

Oh--the shame of it! Toad in women's clothes!

PENELOPE

But isn't it clever? Sort of a masquerade. Now the
apron.

> (Ties it on)

TOAD
(Brightens)

That's right. It *is* a masquerade and I *am* being

clever, aren't I?

                    PENELOPE
Certainly! And now the shawl----
                    (Arranges it)

                    TOAD
                    (Sagging)
Wait a bit----

                    PENELOPE
And tie the bonnet strings.
                    (Steps back to look at the full effect)
There! You're the very image of her, only I'm sure
you never looked half so respectable in your life before!

                    (TOAD sinks to a stool)

                    TOAD
It won't work.

                    PENELOPE
Why not? The guard will never give you a second
look.

                    TOAD
I'll be missed. They'll see my empty cell. There'll
be a hue and cry!

                    PENELOPE
Oh, no, they won't.
                    (Reaches into the basket)
See these pillows? We'll stuff them into your weskit
and coat--so. Help me, please.
                    (He springs to do so)
And arrange them in the bed--so! Anyone looking in
will see Mr. Toad is taking a nap.

TOAD

Excellent girl! You've thought of everything.
        (Sinks to a stool)
No.

PENELOPE

What now!

TOAD

My honor as a gentleman. I can't let you take the
blame for my escape.

PENELOPE

Silly Toad! I've thought of that, too.   Take this
string----
        (He does so)
--and I'll sit upon this stool, and you tie my hands
behind me.   Then put this gag in my mouth. I'll
say that Mr. Toad overpowered me while I was feed-
ing him.   Now take the laundry basket and scurry
along!

TOAD

Ingenious lass!
        (He sets to work tying her hands as instruct-
        ed, but pauses)
But why are you doing all this? For me?

PENELOPE

It's only partly for you. I read the letter downstairs,
before I brought it up to you. It's the rules here.

TOAD

I see----

PENELOPE

And that about poor Mrs. Otter wrung my heart.
        (Speaks pleadingly)
Promise me you'll be very clever and rescue her little boy!

CURTAIN

ACT TWO
Scene One

A partial cut-out of an antique British locomotive is seen as if drawn up at a station
platform. The two dimensional cut-out is
designed so that there is extra space be-
tween the tender and the engine-driver's
position, in which the actors may move a-
bout.

ALF and BILL, the engine-driver and fireman, respectively, are lounging in the cab
waiting for the signal to depart the station.
It is night and the glow from the engine
shows red.

BILL
(Leaning out on the engine-driver's side)
I say, Alf, what's holding us at Tinkersley so long?

ALF
Week-end picnic crowd, lad. Squeezing into the
coaches! We'll be fair delayed.

BILL
Say! Look at the old biddy bearing down on us! Bet
she's going to warn us to drive safely!

ALF
Hold your jaw, lad and talk respectful of your elders.
Here she comes now.

(TOAD enters, now playing the role of "washerwoman" to the hilt. He has "her" belongings tied up in a bundle. The bundle contains some of Toad's discarded gentleman's clothes. TOAD leans against the side of the locomotive tender and uses "her" handkerchief pitiably)

ALF
Hullo, mother! What's the trouble?

BILL
(Muttering)
Looks a mess, if you asks me!

ALF
(Warning)
Mind, lad!
(To TOAD)
Don't take no notice of him. No manners.

TOAD
(Crying afresh)
Oh, sir! I am a poor unhappy washerwoman, and I've lost all my money, and can't pay for a ticket, and I *must* get home tonight, and whatever I am to do I don't know. Oh, dear, oh, dear!

BILL
(Wisely)
That'll get 'round the old 'un!

ALF
(To BILL)
Be off!
(BILL retires to the fireman's side of the cab)

Now, madam, that's a bad business indeed.   Lost
your money--and can't get home!   Got some kids,
too, waiting for you, I dare say?

TOAD
Any amount of them.   And if I don't get home, they'll
be hungry--and playing with matches--and upsetting
lamps, the little innocents!   Oh, dear!   Oh, dear!

ALF
(Wiping aside a tear)
Puts me in mind of my own old mother, she does!

TOAD
Bless you, my boy.   I seen you was gold clear through,
or I shouldn't have come down to your engine to pester you.

ALF
Pester?   Not a bit of it.   Tell you what I'll do.   I'm
an engine-driver, and my job gets a lot of shirts
dirty, as you may well see.   If you'll wash a few
shirts for me when you get home, and send 'em along,
I'll give you a ride on my engine.   It's against com-
pany regulations, but they'll likely never hear of it.
(The guard's whistle blows--a sound like
that of an American policeman's whistle--
indicating that the train should start on its
way)
Here we go!   Hop aboard, my lady!
(TOAD nimbly hops on, and leans against
the inside edge of the tender)
Now hold on tight.
(Whistle sound--a "tweet"--and sound of
the engine starting up and gaining speed)

TOAD
My!   You've got a wonderful sleek beauty of an engine,

driver!

ALF
Aye, she's old but she was built for speed. Swiftest on the line, in her better days. I'll let her out a little.
(Engine sounds: faster)

TOAD
(Himself again)
Travel, excitement, adventure!

ALF
(Surprised at Toad's voice)
You caught a bit of a cold, mother? That's an awful hoarse voice you had just then.

TOAD
(Remembering to speak like an old lady)
My throat again, lad. It goes in and out like that on me. My old ailment.

ALF
A bit of flannel with camphor on it'll soon ease that.

TOAD
(Glancing nervously to the rear)
I'd be pleased if you'd push along a bit faster.

ALF
Hang on, we'll try!
(Shouts)
More coal, Bill!

BILL
(From the shadows)
My back's fair breaking on me now!

ALF

Save your breath and swing the shovel.
          (Pulls the whistle cord: "Tweet-tweet!")

TOAD
          (Excited)
That's even better than "Poop-poop!"

ALF

What say, mother?

TOAD

Nothin', my lad.
          (Shouts)
More coal, Bill!

BILL
          (From the shadows)
You mind your knittin', mother!

ALF

Bill! Watch it, I say!

TOAD
          (Singing)
Oh, riding the rails is tolerably sweet
As we nip right along to the engine's tweet-tweet!
          (ALF pulls the whistle cord)

ALF

That's right, mother, sing away!

TOAD
          (Singing)
Across the meadow and over the hill
And Toad will have supper at home, he will!

1

ALF
Who's that? What's that about a toad?

TOAD
(Coughing)
Nothing, my son. Just a snatch of an old nursery rhyme.
> (Excited, BILL comes over to the driver's side)

BILL
Oy! Alf! When we swing 'round the next curve, give a look back and see if you see what I just seen!

ALF
What, boy?

BILL
I seen another engine, down the line, following us!

ALF
Come off it, Billy, my lad. We're the last train this direction tonight.

BILL
Stone me if I ain't telling the truth, Alfie! Here we go 'round the curve of your side. Look what's following us!
> (Glares at TOAD)
Say! The old lady's gone green! She's carsick.
> (TOAD tries to hide his face. He looks to rearward also, where headlight of another train shows)

ALF
(Peering toward the rear of the train)
I can see a headlight.

BILL
Didn't I tell you so?

ALF
It's an engine, on our rails, coming fast! Looks as
if they're chasing us!

TOAD
Oh, mercy!

BILL
(On his side of the engine)
They're gaining fast!   ?er l?? of people in helmets
sticking their heads out.
(Sound of gunfire)

ALF
They're shooting off pistols into the air!

BILL
They're signaling us to stop!

ALF
Better shout than shoot, says I!

TOAD
(Terrified; in his natural voice)
Don't stop! Don't stop, I beg you!
(Catches himself; speaks in the old-woman
voice)
Don't stop! Please----

BILL
(Glowering down at TOAD)
Say, you don't sound like no old lady to me!

TOAD
Oh, sir, you're so unkind!

ALF
(His eyes on the rails)
Don't be hard on the old woman, Bill.

TOAD
(Enthusiastic agreement, in his own voice)
Yes!   Don't be hard on the old woman . . . ulp.
(As the men turn to stare at him, he vainly
raises his voice to a squeak)
. . . gentlemen . . .
(In toying with the bonnet strings, he has
loosened them)

BILL
(Flipping off the bonnet)
This ain't no old woman!

ALF
I *see* it ain't!   See here, now! . . .
(TOAD falls to his knees and raises his
clasped paws in supplication)

TOAD
Save me, only save me, dear kind engine-driver, and
I will confess everything!   I am not a washerwoman.
I am Toad, a landed proprietor.   I have just escaped
prison, by my great daring and cleverness.   And if
those fellows recapture me, it will be chains and mis-
ery once more for poor, unhappy, innocent Toad!

BILL
(Looking at TOAD with more interest)
Cor! A gentleman criminal!   How many has you
murdered, sir?

TOAD
Murdered? Oh, not that.

ALF

Shut up, Bill!
        (To TOAD)
Now tell the truth. What were you put in prison for?

TOAD

I only borrowed a limousine while the owners were
at lunch.

BILL

Copped a limousine?
        (Laughs)
Lor', that's rich!

ALF

Bill!

BILL

Who cares what happens to our competition?

ALF

True, I don't hold with cars. People should travel
on trains.

TOAD
        (Quickly)
My sentiments exactly. Now a great puffing steam
locomotive has ever so much more zip and go.

BILL

Alf, this bloke's all right, says I.

ALF
        (To TOAD)
I fear I ought to give you up to justice.

BILL

Blimey! Pour on coal and give them the slip, says I!

TOAD

Right! Right!
          (To ALF)
Listen to *him*.

ALF

But since it was only a limousine--and I don't hold
with them--and since I don't hold with being ordered
about on my own engine---- Yes! Pour on coal, Bill!
          (Pulls the whistle cord: "Tweet-tweet!")

TOAD

Oh, thank you! Thank you, kind engine-driver.
          (Shouts)
Pour on coal, Bill!

BILL

          (Shoveling with fury)
Right, old lady!
          (The men laugh at this, and the chase moves
          to a crescendo of excitement and sound.
          TOAD leans out and looks back along the
          tender. The light of the approaching head-
          light grows brighter)

TOAD

Faster! Faster! They're gaining!

ALF

          (A brief look back)
So they are. More coal, Bill!

TOAD

They're closer!

BILL

I'm shoveling all I can!

ALF
(Turning and wiping his brow)
I'm afraid it's no good, Toad. They're running light,
and I've got all these cars to pull!

TOAD
It'll be jail for me?

BILL
(Looming over TOAD)
What's to do?

ALF
There's just one thing left to do, and it's our only
chance. So listen carefully, Toad. There's a long
tunnel coming up soon----

BILL
I know the one.

ALF
--and on the other side, a thick wood. We'll dash
through the tunnel, then slam on the brakes and let
you jump out and hide in the woods!

BILL
Good show, Alfie! You've got a head on you!

ALF
(To TOAD)
Now, mind, and be ready to jump when I tell you!

BILL
Pull in your heads! Here's the tunnel!
(The stage goes black, showing that the
engine is now going through the tunnel. Suddenly the engine is through the tunnel, and

into the light again)

ALF
(Yelling)
Down brakes!
(To TOAD)
Now--ready?

TOAD
(On Bill's side of the engine)
Ready. But isn't that a river down there?

ALF
(Giving him a push)

Jump!
(TOAD gives a yowl as he disappears behind
the locomotive on Bill's side)

BILL
Blimey, Alf! You forgot the river!

ALF
(Peering down)
Lor' love a duck! He'll drown!
(Toad's voice is heard in the distance: "Ah
--oh! Help!")

BILL
(Peering over Alf's shoulder)
He's bobbing up!

ALF
(Shouting)
Good luck, Toad!

BILL
He's swimming--I think he'll make it.

ALF

Full speed ahead, Bill!

> (The engine chuffs into faster action, and
> BILL yanks the whistle cord: "Tweet-
> tweet!")

CURTAIN

ACT TWO

Scene Two

The scene is played before the curtain. As
the theatre darkens there is the sound of
flute music ending in scattered bird calls.
As the lights come on we see a sign reading:

WILD WOOD
DANGER

However, the scene is attractive rather than
ominous. Some willow branches in concealed
pots supply the effect of free-standing trees
and some flowers in concealed pots give a
further woodland touch.

JACK and JEN WEASEL enter R. JACK has
a short whip in his hand.

JEN WEASEL

(Whining and limping)

Don't walk so fast.

JACK WEASEL
(Sourly)
If you'd worn sneakers like I said, you wouldn't of sprained your ankle. Come along now!

JEN WEASEL
I've got to rest a minute.
(Sits on a tree stump)
You always want to be boss.

JACK WEASEL
(Arrogantly)
Who's got a better right? It's thanks to me we're living high at Toad Hall.

JEN WEASEL
(Rubbing her ankle)
We *were* living high at Toad Hall until you started giving yourself airs and all the servants quit.

JACK WEASEL
(Sharply)
They were a lazy lot, anyway. Once I get my paws on Portly Otter, I can train him to do most of the work. Come along. We've got to find that kid before someone else finds him and takes him home.

JEN WEASEL
(Trying to stand and sinking down again)
Ouch!

JACK WEASEL
(Relenting)
Oh, well, we may as well rest here a bit. Tom and Tilly'll be along soon.
(Glances off L)
Let's hope they've seen Portly.

JEN WEASEL
(Petulantly)
I don't think your idea's much good, anyway. Portly
isn't old enough to work. And it'll cost the earth to
feed him!

JACK WEASEL
The trouble with you, Jen, is that you're thinking
of the kid as if he were a young weasel. There, I
admit, you've got to be careful. A young weasel must
have time to play and plenty of good food. But otters
aren't like weasels. It's a kindness to teach Portly
to work. It's all he's good for, and we'll give him
table scraps to eat.

JEN WEASEL
He won't touch them. Mrs. Otter says he's very
particular about what he eats.

JACK WEASEL
(Smugly)
He'll eat the scraps and beg for more. And as for
the work----
(Taps his whip significantly)
--he'll work, and work fast.

JEN WEASEL
I expect you're right. I'll see if I can walk now.
(Stands experimentally and takes a pace or
two back and forth. Pauses as she turns to-
ward entrance R and speaks sharply)
Someone's coming.

(MRS. OTTER enters R. She seems nerv-
ous and under emotional strain. She hesi-
tates as she sees the WEASELS and then
comes forward)

MRS. OTTER
Mrs. Weasel, Mr. Weasel, have you seen anything
of Portly?

JACK WEASEL
Portly? Why, I don't know if I'd recognize him if I
saw him.
> (To JEN WEASEL)
Have you seen Mrs. Otter's boy, dear?

JEN WEASEL
> (With false friendliness)
Oh, dear, Mrs. Otter, I've been looking around every-
where I go for the little darling. I *know* he's not on
the main path back there.
> (Points toward R entrance)
But now I remember seeing some paw marks where
the little path led into the wood. Did you look there?

MRS. OTTER
> (Slightly wringing her paws)
No--no, I hardly noticed the little path! How far back
would you say it is?

JACK WEASEL
About half a mile.

MRS. OTTER
Then, if you will kindly excuse me, I'll hurry straight
back.
> (Turns hastily to go R)

JACK WEASEL
Good luck.
> (Smirks knowingly at JEN WEASEL)

JEN WEASEL
Let us know when you find him!

(Grins at JACK WEASEL)

MRS. OTTER

Thank you for your kindness in directing me! I'll
surely let you know--kind, true friends that you are!
(She hurries out R)

JACK WEASEL

What did I tell you? Otters have no brains.   It'll be
a kindness to the kid to train him to obey orders.
(Swings his whip as if striking a small
animal. Offstage L we hear three short,
sharp whistles. He is suddenly alert)
That'll be Tom and Tilly!
(Gives a long and a short whistle)

(TOM and TILLY WEASEL enter L)

TOM WEASEL
(Eagerly)
We've got the kid spotted. He's coming this way!

TILLY WEASEL
(Angrily)
A pretty chore it was tracking him. He's wandering
all over.
(Sneeringly)
Picking flowers for his mommy!

JEN WEASEL
(Cheerfully)
Never mind all that! No more dishwashing for you
and me!

TILLY WEASEL
(Also happy)

No more making beds and setting the table!

                    JEN WEASEL
No more sweeping and dusting.

                    JACK WEASEL
          (Sharply)
First we catch him and get him back to Toad Hall
before anyone sees us.   Here, you, spread out. He
won't notice you unless you move, so don't stir until
I give the whistle.

                    TOM WEASEL
And then?

                    JACK WEASEL
We rush him, throw the jacket over his head and
cart him off to Toad Hall----
          (Waves his whip)
--and start training him to be of some use in the
world.

               (The four WEASELS separate near the
               entrance L and stand motionless. PORTLY
               enters L.   He has a handful of flowers in
               his hand and may be humming happily to him-
               self.   He spies the flowers and crosses to
               pick them.   JACK WEASEL gives a short,
               sharp whistle.   The four WEASELS swoop
               down on PORTLY, throw a jacket over his
               head and force him, struggling, to the floor.
               There they quickly truss him up and with
               furtive looks R over their shoulders, pick
               up PORTLY--still trying to escape--and
               exit L with him)

                    BLACKOUT

ACT TWO

Scene Three

The living room of Rat's comfortable home by the riverside. There are chairs, coffee tables, etc., and a fireplace.

RAT and MOLE are seated, taking tea. MRS. OTTER is pacing the floor, having left her cup of tea by her chair.

RAT
My dear Mrs. Otter! Pray sit down and drink your tea.

MRS. OTTER
Tea? At a time like this? With little Portly in danger!

MOLE
But we *must* wait for Badger.

MRS. OTTER
(Starting out)
I'm going to Toad Hall *now*, and insist on going in!

RAT
(Quickly moving to restrain her)
My dear Mrs. Otter! Please be patient. If we are going to help Portly we must have a plan.

MOLE

We *must* wait for Badger.

RAT

Directly I'd told him the news about Portly, he sped
off to Toad Hall. Said he had to spy out the lay of the
land.

MRS. OTTER
(Despairing)

But what can he do? What can even *four* of us do,
against so many?

MOLE

I don't know. But Badger is shrewd. Always thinking, thinking. No one's ever got the better of him,
in the end.

RAT

Drink your tea, Mrs. Otter. It'll warm you for whatever business we have to do tonight. I'll keep a look-
out for Badger here at the window.

MRS. OTTER
(Wiping her eyes)

Very well.
(Drinks a little tea. Speaks apologetically)
It's not sleeping nights that gets me so unstrung!
(Rubs her eyes)
I shan't wait much longer.
(Despairing, hides her face in her hands)

MOLE

Depend on Badger.

RAT
(Suddenly tense)

Mole!

MOLE

What is it?

RAT

It can't be! There's an old lady swimming in the
river--with all her clothes on!

MOLE

No accounting for tastes.

RAT

Now she's up! Now she's under----
        (Off, Toad's voice: "Help! Ah--oo--oo!")

MOLE

A deep-voiced old lady.

RAT

She's in trouble. I'll run help her.
        (RAT rushes out. MOLE runs to the win-
        dow)

MOLE

        (Shouting)
That way, Ratty. Good show! You've got her!
        (Runs to door and calls out)
Bring her on in by the fire! Is she hurt?
        (Rat's voice is heard, but not clearly)
What's that?
        (Excited)
Toad? Toad!

        (RAT and TOAD enter, RAT supporting
        TOAD, who is still unsteady. MOLE takes
        Toad's arm and aids RAT in guiding him

to his chair)

MOLE
Hooray! Here's old Toad! You escaped! You clever, ingenious, intelligent Toad! But what are these strange garments?

RAT
Hush, Mole. Can't you see he's all in?
(To TOAD)
Are you all right?

TOAD
(Managing to speak)
Oh, Ratty! Oh, Mole! I've been through such times since I saw you last! Such trials, such sufferings, and all so nobly borne! Then--a disguise--this washerwoman's costume--and escape--all so cleverly planned and carried out! A stolen ride on a locomotive--pursuit by another locomotive, loaded with police--a leap into the river----

MOLE
Clever Toad! Intelligent Toad--escaped as a washerwoman!

TOAD
(Brightening)
Oh, I *am* a smart Toad, and no mistake----

RAT
(Severely)
Toad! Stop rattling on. Here's Mrs. Otter.

TOAD
(Soberly approaching MRS. OTTER)
My dear Mrs. Otter . . .

MRS. OTTER
(Looking up)
Mr. Toad? Is it indeed you?

TOAD
Yes. Broke out of prison, especially to help find young Portly and to drive those weasels out of Toad Hall.

RAT
You can do both at the same time, for the weasels have Portly at Toad Hall. But we must wait for Badger. Mole, bring Toad a cup of tea. Stand by the fire, Toad, and let your clothes dry.
(MOLE exits)

TOAD
But, Ratty, I do look a fright.

RAT
(Grim)
You look a *fool*. And that's what you've been making of yourself.

(MOLE brings TOAD a cup of tea and a biscuit and sets them on the mantel. TOAD meekly begins sipping tea a..d eating the biscuit)

TOAD
You're quite right, Ratty. I've been a fool. But I promise I'll reform. And as soon as I've some dry clothes on, we'll go down to Toad Hall and drive those weasels out!

RAT
Not so fast! They have sentinels with guns.

TOAD
(Dismayed)
Guns?

MOLE
And Rat was terribly beaten----

RAT
And Badger's there now, spying out the land----

MOLE
All of us, trying to preserve your property for you
--but the main thing is to get Portly from them.

TOAD
Portly in their hands!
(Wipes a tear from his eyes)
Let me start at once before they kill the child!

MRS. OTTER
(Rising)
Yes, let's go at once.

RAT
Stuff! What could either of you do against their guns?
You don't help Portly by getting yourselves killed!
(MRS. OTTER sinks down again and hides
her face in her hands. There is a knock
at the door)
That's Badger!

(RAT goes to the door and admits BADGER)

RAT
Come in, dear old Badger! We have a jolly surprise
for you. Toad's home!
(TOAD rushes over to shake hands with

BADGER)

BADGER
(Solemnly)
So I see. What's this, a masquerade?

TOAD
I'm dressed as a washerwoman. This is how I escaped from prison. Clever of me, eh?

BADGER
You'd have been cleverer still, not to have got there
in the first place.
>(BADGER turns away from the embarrassed
>TOAD, who retreats to the fireplace. BADG-
>ER approaches MRS. OTTER, and places
>his hand on her shoulder)

Mrs. Otter, I've found the way to rescue Portly.
Rest assured, we shall do it tonight. Now I'm going
to tell you a great secret.
>(The others sit up straight to listen)

There--is--an--underground--passage! It leads
from the river bank, quite near here, right up into
the middle of Toad Hall. I have just checked, and
the passage is still open.

TOAD
(Conceitedly)
Oh, nonsense, Badger. I know every inch of Toad
Hall, inside and out. There's nothing of the sort,
I assure you!

BADGER
(Severely)
My young friend, your father showed me this ancient
passage years ago. "Don't let my son know about
it, " he said. "He's a good boy, but simply cannot

hold his tongue. If he's ever in real danger, and could use the secret passage, you may tell him about it, but not before."
>   (The others stare hard at TOAD)

TOAD
>   (Embarrassed)
Well, well--perhaps I am a bit of a talker.
>   (Brightens)
A popular fellow such as I am----
>   (Wilts under Badger's stern glance)
--talks a lot.

BADGER
Now! Remove those ridiculous garments, so that I may feel I'm speaking to an English gentleman toad, capable of action and daring!

TOAD
If you'll excuse me, ma'am.
>   (MRS. OTTER bows assent and modestly
>   turns away as TOAD begins to remove the
>   bonnet, shawl, apron and dress)

BADGER
Meanwhile, I'll tell you what I've learned by tonight's spying. The weasels are having a great banquet. The stoat sentries are very angry at being left out of the party to stand guard. The place is *ripe* for invasion.
>   (TOAD is revealed in shirt and trousers.
>   MOLE holds the items of the woman's cos-
>   tume)

We must strike tonight! All the weasels will be eating and drinking and carrying on, suspecting nothing. No guns, no swords, no arms of any sort whatsoever!

RAT

But the sentinels?

BADGER

The secret passage will allow us to by-pass them.
The tunnel leads right up under the butler's pantry,
next to the dining hall.

TOAD

Aha! That squeaky board in the butler's pantry!

MRS. OTTER

If only Portly's still safe!

BADGER

I saw him pass a window, carrying a very heavy
tray! We don't have to worry about Portly's doing
his part.

MOLE

(Savagely)

We shall creep quietly into the butler's pantry----

TOAD

(Shouting)

--with our swords and pistols and sticks----

BADGER

--and rush in upon them----

TOAD

(Jumping over a chair in ecstasy)

--and whack 'em, and whack 'em, and whack 'em!

RAT

To arms!

(Blankly)

But where will we get arms?

BADGER
I've gathered all we'll need and hidden them near the
entrance of the tunnel.

MOLE
Good old Badger! Thinks of everything!

BADGER
Lanterns for everyone!
    (RAT runs out)

TOAD
Lanterns? Pooh! What do we need lanterns for?

BADGER
We shall need them in the tunnel.

TOAD
Oh--yes--the tunnel.

BADGER
Now *do* put your mind to this, Toad.

    (RAT comes in with five glowing "dark-
    lanterns" which have slotted covers. He
    hands one to each of his friends and keeps
    one. The five animals raise their lanterns
    and touch them together)

ALL
One for all, and all for----

TOAD
    (Loud)
--Toad!

(The others glare at him)

CURTAIN

ACT TWO
Scene Four

This scene is played before the curtain.
Lights are dimmed down. The scene re-
quires nothing except the properties men-
tioned in the lines and one additional thing,
a slanted ladder lying on its side and covered with a tarpaulin to make a handy ramp
for climbing up into the supposed tunnel. It
is placed at one side of the stage.

BADGER, MOLE, MRS. OTTER, RAT, and
TOAD enter at one side of the stage, carrying sticks and the dark-lanterns.

BADGER

Aye, here we are! Now, Mrs. Otter, I think it's
best for you to stay here. You can keep some soup
hot for Portly when we bring him back.

MRS. OTTER
(Quietly and firmly)
I'm going with you.

BADGER
But you don't know how to handle weapons--do you?

MRS. OTTER

No--but I have my broom.
> (Shows it)

RAT

> (Scornfully)

A broom!

MRS. OTTER

> (Defensively)

You can do a lot with a broom.

BADGER

> (Meeting her determined glance for a mo-
> ment)

Very well.
> (Removes the tarpaulin which covers the
> cache of weapons)

We should be able to subdue these ruffians with our
sticks, and Mrs. Otter's broom. But just in case--
here's a belt and pistol for Mole----
> (Hands the items to MOLE, who straps on
> the belt and stuffs the pistol under it)

A belt and pistol for Ratty----
> (Hands them to RAT)

And a belt and pistol for Toad----
> (Hands these items to TOAD. TOAD straps
> on the belt and then waves his pistol in the
> air)

TOAD

Is it loaded? Let's try----
> (The others go for him and pull his arm
> down)

BADGER

No!

TOAD

Not loaded?

BADGER

Yes. Loaded. Don't wave it about so. It might go off.

TOAD

True.
          (To the others)
Be careful of the pistols, fellows.
          (The others groan)

BADGER

Now, each take a cutlass and attach it to your belts.
          (Passes these items out)
Now! Line up to enter the secret passage. Mole first----

MRS. OTTER

I should go first! He's my son----

BADGER

          (Firmly)
Mole first. He's best suited for it, from long experience at burrowing underground.

MOLE

          (Happy)
You mean, I'm an expert at something? How jolly!

BADGER

Then I, then Mrs. Otter, then Rat, and last, Toad.

TOAD

Last!

BADGER
(Weary)
It's a position of honor. You're the rear guard.

TOAD
(Giggling)
Oh, very clever of you to realize my importance.

BADGER
Look here, Toady! Stop your chatter or you'll be
sent back, sure as fate!
    (To the others)
Now, men! Into the entrance!
    (MOLE, BADGER, MRS. OTTER, and then
    RAT kneel down and crawl on all fours, as
    if in a low tunnel. TOAD kneels down and
    crawls quickly after the others, who are
    making careful, slow progress. There is
    a yowl of pain from RAT, who plunges into
    MRS. OTTER, who shoves BADGER, who
    knocks MOLE down. A chorus of "Sh! Sh!")

BADGER
Whatever is all the commotion?

RAT
It's Toad. He stuck me with his cutlass!

BADGER
Toad, I warn you.
    (They proceed)

MOLE
The passage turns sharply upward here!
    (He starts up the ladder, and the others fol-
    low. Soon all are groping upward)

Sh! We're right under them!
> (Sounds from above: stamping of feet, and
> voices of the weasels: "Oooo--ray--oo--
> ray--oo--ray!")

BADGER
What a time they're having. Push on, Mole.
> (The first four animals move on up and out
> of sight. TOAD pauses at the top of the lad-
> der)

TOAD
I'll give them something to shout about!
> (From above, his companions shush him.
> He moves on up and out of sight. The stage
> is dark)

BLACKOUT

ACT TWO
Scene Five

> The butler's pantry of Toad Hall is really a
> rather large room, with a fireplace. On
> either side of the fireplace is a door. Each
> of these doors opens into the banqueting hall,
> so that if one opens either door a crack to
> listen, one hears quite clearly what is go-
> ing on in there. Curtain entrances D L and
> D R are assumed to be other doors to the
> room. The D L entrance leads to the kitchen.

MOLE, BADGER, MRS. OTTER, RAT and TOAD enter D R, shushing each other. Inside the banqueting hall there is much noise: cheering, handclapping, etc. MOLE opens the right door a crack, and RAT opens the left door. TOAD is at Rat's shoulder. The voice of JACK WEASEL serving as chairman is heard.

JACK WEASEL
(Offstage)
We all know how much we owe to Mr. Toad----
(Laughter)
Remember?
(A familiar "Poop-poop" is heard)
--who will not be with us for twenty years----
(Laughter)
--so I want you to hear a little song which I have composed on the subject of Toad.
(Applause)

TOAD
Only just let me get at him!
(RAT restrains TOAD.   JACK WEASEL sings)

JACK WEASEL
Toad he went a-tootling
(Sounds horn: "Poop-poop!")
Gaily down the street,
Banging into everything
His motor car did meet!
(Sounds horn again: "Poop-poop!")

TOAD
(In a frenzy of anger)
Oooh! I'll *teach* him to sing!

BADGER
(In a hoarse whisper)
Hide! Quick! Someone's coming!
(The five invading animals duck behind cur-
tains downstage)

(The WEASEL COOK, a fat lady weasel
wearing an apron, enters from D L and goes
to the left door, opens it, and bawls a com-
mand)

WEASEL COOK
Portly Otter! You're wanted in the kitchen!

VOICES
(Offstage)
Portly Otter! Hop it, Portly! You want a touch of
the whip again?
(The WEASEL COOK starts back toward the
door D L. In a flash of daring, TOAD looms
up behind her, claps his hand over her
mouth. RAT rushes out to help him, and
the other animals join in overpowering her,
gagging her, and tying her to a chair. MOLE
and RAT drag the chair and its surprised
occupant offstage D L)

BADGER
Make no noise! Toad, that was rash!

TOAD
But wasn't I clever?

MRS. OTTER
He's alive! Portly's alive!
(Wipes her eyes as tears of happiness come)

(MOLE and RAT return from D L)

BADGER
But how shall we *keep* him from being harmed, when the fighting begins? Toad, you've upset my plans!

TOAD
Then I'll show you something *else*. I've had experience, lately, imitating old women's voices!
(Steps to left door and opens it slightly)

BADGER
Toad! No----

TOAD
(Not to be stopped, he bawls, in imitation of the cook's voice)
Portly Otter! You lazy brat! You're wanted in the kitchen!

RAT
(Tensely)
Oh, mercy! What if one of the weasels----

(But it is PORTLY, wearing an apron and carrying a tray, who enters the door. He stares at the group, then sees what the situation is)

PORTLY
(Dropping his tray and running to MRS. OTTER)
Mama!

TOAD
Quick, Mrs. Otter. Hide Portly in the tunnel, where he'll be safe!

(MRS. OTTER and PORTLY quickly exit)

BADGER

We must attack now! They've heard the tray bang!
(BADGER flings the door open and hurls
himself into the banqueting hall. RAT,
MOLE, and TOAD follow. Offstage we hear
squeals of rage and pain, fighting, chairs
and tables being overturned, throughout the
balance of the scene until the weasels are
defeated)

(JACK WEASEL darts in right door, followed by TOAD, who is chasing him with
his stick. JACK has the car horn in his
hand)

TOAD

Whack, sir! Whack! Whack!
(They disappear out left door. JACK drops
the car horn unnoticed)

(TOM WEASEL and TILLY come rushing in
right door, followed by the angry BADGER
and RAT)

BADGER

Stop! You villains.
(But TOM and TILLY rush off L. BADGER
pants)
Go after them, Rat.
(Panting)
Watch out for the stoat guards!

RAT

(Shouting back as he goes)

I will!

BADGER
(Panting)
Got to see if Mole's all right.
(Rushes back out right door)

(JACK WEASEL slinks back in)

JACK WEASEL
Give him the slip, I did.
(Gives two sharp whistles)
Jen.

(JEN WEASEL enters)

JEN WEASEL
That Badger, he'll kill us. Let's get out.

JACK WEASEL
Steady on, old girl, we'll get the best of them yet.
Sound the alarm for the stoat guards. I can't under-
stand why they haven't heard the uproar.

JEN WEASEL
Probably playing poker. I'll ring the alarm.
(She crosses quickly off L and shortly an
alarm bell begins to sound)

JACK WEASEL
And now to settle with Toad once for all!
(Snatches up a cutlass and goes off R)

(There is a crash of china from the dining
room and TOAD enters, waving his stick
and dragging a tablecloth)

TOAD
(Fiercely)

That'll settle their banquet for them. *My* tablecloth!
My food! Toad Hall all being used by filthy weasels!
(Suddenly TOAD hears shrill whistles. Instantly he reacts. He kneels on one knee,
tablecloth over him, holding out his arms
under it so that he now resembles an arm
chair with a dust cover over it)

(JACK and JEN WEASEL enter from L and
R)

JACK WEASEL
(Greatly agitated)

What's the matter with the stoat guards? Didn't they
hear the alarm? Where are they?

JEN WEASEL
(Despondent)

All gone! Not one of them's left.

JACK WEASEL

Then call the two fox sentries. Slip out the back door.

JEN WEASEL

Why don't you get them? They're likelier to come
for you!

JACK WEASEL

Because I've got to get Toad at any cost.
(Sharply)

On your way! Hurry!
(JEN WEASEL runs out. JACK WEASEL
strides up and down, worried)

A plan! If I only had a plan!
(He approaches the chair and then turns away)

I've got to think of a plan.
> (Strikes his head in despair. Strides down-
> stage and then turns and again approaches
> the chair.   Speaks to himself in tones of
> admonition)

Now, Jack, be a smart weasel. Sit down in this
chair, take a deep breath and *think*.
> (JACK WEASEL sits down.   Instantly the
> "chair arms" close about him, and he and
> TOAD struggle.   Then the fight suddenly
> goes out of JACK WEASEL. He sinks to the
> floor in front of TOAD, the picture of blub-
> bering misery)

JACK WEASEL
Spare me! Spare me!

TOAD
Why should I spare you?
> (Raises stick higher)

> (JEN WEASEL whistles shrilly and enters)

JEN WEASEL
The foxes are gone, too! And Badger's coming this
way with all our friends!

BADGER
> (Offstage)

This way! Step lively.

> (TOM and TILLY WEASEL enter, with MOLE
> and RAT on guard behind them.   BADGER
> follows them on)

BADGER
Oh, I see you've got the rest of the leaders, Toad.

     (To JACK and JEN WEASEL)

Fall in line, you!

     (JACK and JEN fall in line with TILLY and
     TOM)

Now, off you go to the police! They're waiting outside
ready for you.

JACK WEASEL
     (Glib as always)

Aw, guvnor, not the police! We'll leave the country
peaceable-like.

BADGER

Certainly, to the police. Keep your guns steady, men.
Now march. The police are waiting with a van so
don't try any tricks!

     (The WEASELS are marched off. Outside
     there is the sound of a car door slamming
     and a car starting)

     (MOLE, RAT, BADGER, MRS. OTTER and
     PORTLY enter)

ALL

Hurrah!

BADGER

Toad Hall is ours!

MRS. OTTER

My son!

BADGER

The stoats all fled in panic!

MOLE

And Portly's safe!

ALL

Hurrah!

MRS. OTTER

Thank you kindly, all of you--and little Portly joins
me in this--for your courage and cleverness.

BADGER

Thank Toad, most daring of all!

TOAD

Why--why--Badger! That's very handsome of you.
          (Struts a bit)
Yes! And tomorrow night we must all banquet togeth-
er. Send out invitations to the entire animal commu-
nity. First, I'll give a speech. Then I'll sing a song,
something along these lines:

The Toad--came--home!
There was panic in the parlor and howling in the hall,
There was crying in the cow-shed and shrieking in
    the stall,
When the Toad--came--home!

                    (Unseen by TOAD, BADGER has given the
                    wink to RAT and MOLE, and has taken the
                    washerwoman costume out of a sack and
                    has it at the ready)
Bang! go the drums!
As the Hero comes!

BADGER

Now!

                    (RAT and MOLE spring on TOAD, and hold
                    him while BADGER invests him with the wash-
                    erwoman costume)
Now! If you don't tone down a peg, *this* is how you
shall appear at the banquet.

TOAD
(Miserable)
What's the matter, fellows? Don't you like my song?
Wasn't it loud enough?

RAT
No, we don't like your song. All *gas* and vanity. But
we like you----

BADGER
If you promise to reform.

RAT
No more boasting.

MOLE
No more rows with the police.

BADGER
No more cars!

RAT
Promise, and we'll hire lawyers to persuade the Magistrate to try you again----

BADGER
--and you shall offer to pay just damages to all injured
parties.

TOAD
Enough! You have conquered, my dear friends.

BADGER
Remove those garments, Mole and Rat.
(They do so)

TOAD
(Takes Badger's hand)

It is enough for me, to be reunited with my
friends, and----
> (Hugs PORTLY)

--to have this fellow back with us again.
> (PORTLY laughs, wriggles free, and clasps
> his mother's hand. Expansively:)

And now, as it's a long, dark way home for all of
you, you must stay with me this night at Toad Hall!

BADGER
> (At door)

Oh, we'll stay longer than that----

RAT
> (With BADGER, MOLE, MRS. OTTER and
> PORTLY at door)

--to see that you don't go wrong.
> (All leave the room)

TOAD
Quite right, chaps! But--you'll see--I'm truly reformed.
> (The other have gone, and TOAD is left
> alone on stage. He pauses, then steps down
> to audience)

Reformed?
> (Takes a deep breath and holds it so that
> his cheeks blow out)

Sounds awfully dull, but I suppose----
> (His glance lights on the car horn lying where
> Jack Weasel had dropped it)

What--do--I--see?
> (At each word he draws a step nearer)

No, I won't touch it!
> (Covers his eyes with his hand, then uncov-
> ers one eye)

My trusty car horn! Hope they didn't damage it!

(Picks up the horn and examines it)
Looks all right.   Still----
(Suddenly he squeezes the bulb: "Poop-poop!"
Capers and follows after his friends)

CURTAIN

NOTES ON CHARACTERS
AND COSTUMES

Children seem to be born with the ability to imagine and should be encouraged to do so.

Thus it is better that representational treatment should be used for the animal-people (Mole, Rat, etc.) than attempt to present them as actual animals. Head or face masks are to be avoided, as they may interfere with clarity of diction. A close-fitting cap with firmly fastened ears, and perhaps a tail, are sufficient for identification. Flexible mittens in the appropriate color identification give the effect of paws.

MOLE: He is shy and gentle but has warmth and loyalty and is a lovable animal. He wears spectacles and tends to peer through them. He may wear a shaped papier-mâché snout which rests on his own nose. A gray velveteen skull cap and smoking jacket or an old gray corduroy jacket with gray slacks gives the desirable casual effect. Remember, in life a mole lives underground, has soft silky gray fur and concealed ears. Because of its habitat it shuns light and may find it painful. Grayish make-up on the face adds to the effect.

RAT: He is outspoken and warm-hearted, slender, active and alert. Rats are of various colors-- gray, brown, black, etc. He may wear a close-fitting cap to which his small neat ears are fastened. Grayish or brownish facial make-up lightly applied is desirable, and stylized rat whiskers may be achieved by drawing three sharp lines back from his mouth on each side of his face. Use a make-up liner or an eyebrow pencil. He may wear a corduroy jacket and slacks in the color selected.

BADGER: He is canny and the natural leader of the animals. His slower, heavier walk and the knobbed stick on which he leans suggest his age. A badger is heavy-set and muscular and has a white streak on its head and white cheeks. Badger may achieve greater bulk by wearing a brown flannel shirt and a cardigan or brown tweed jacket. He wears woolen trousers stuffed into high-topped hiking boots. Outdoors he wears a woolen scarf tucked about his neck. He may wear gray or tan facial make-up and a molded papier-mâché snout resting on his nose but not enclosing it. He may wear a skull cap on which the white streak has been painted. He has a great sense of dignity, shrewdness and responsibility. Note: The effect of a knobbed stick may be obtained by wrapping any walking stick unevenly with black friction tape.

TOAD: He is the gay and irresponsible hero and general good fellow. He usually wears a motoring costume of the period, consisting of a "dust coat," goggles, motoring cap and gauntleted gloves. Otherwise, as country squire, he appears in a greenish coat with perhaps a yellow weskit, and greenish riding breeches and gaiters. In his escape costume as the washerwoman, he wears a black wool bonnet with strings, a shawl, a floor-length print gown and an apron over his shirt and breeches. When he enters in these after the dip in the river, there should be some visible dripping. When they are removed his shirt and breeches are not wet. He may wear a green cap, with no ears showing, and the cap should extend as a neck covering. In making him up, his mouth should be extended at the sides and his eyes should be outlined with flat lines below and curved lines above to give the pop-eyed effect.

WEASELS: The Weasels are a slim, lithe and active lot. They bear a striking resemblance to juvenile delinquents. They are swift and darting in their movements. They live by their wits and by taking advantage of anyone who is not on guard against them. The weasel group is dressed similarly (with

110

the exception of the weasel cook). They wear trim brown uniforms such as a group of cyclists might wear.

MRS. OTTER: She is a widow and a motherly type; and her whole-hearted devotion to Portly makes her very appealing. She wears a long brown print house dress. It may be cut along old-fashioned lines, with a fitted bodice and full skirt.

PORTLY: He is as small a child as can be depended on to carry the part. Or an older child who is rather short may be chosen. Portly is not stupid. He is a shy child, driven by loneliness to hang about his elders. He may carry a yo-yo which he sometimes plays with. He may wear brown shorts, a brown T-shirt or sweater and brown socks and sneakers.

CHAUFFEUR: He is dressed in livery: A double-breasted gray jacket with brass buttons, trousers bound by leather leggings, and a cloth cap with a leather bill. He is an attractive and alert chap, not fooled by Toad.

POLICEMAN: He is a country constable with a beefy complexion and a full mustache. He wears the familiar English "Bobby" helmet, a long blue coat, belted and with brass buttons, and a badge, heavy black shoes, and white gloves. He carries a "billy" club. He has an implacable sense of duty. He is not harsh, simply immovable.

JAILER: He is a gentle, elderly man with a sallow complexion resulting from indoor work and mutton-chop whiskers. He wears a gray sweater, nondescript trousers, and heavy shoes. He carries a large iron ring with many keys on it. He is authoritative but kind and simply does his duty.

PENELOPE: She is the Jailer's pretty daughter. She has the appearance of a simple country lass, but this appearance hides her shrewdness. She may wear a long, yellow Empire dress, slim with puffed sleeves, white stockings and Mary Jane pumps. She has intelligence, charm, cleverness and a warm heart.

BILL: He is the fireman on the locomotive "Jupiter." He is a young fellow with a ruddy complexion. Because of his profession, his face is streaked with coal-dust smudges. He wears a blue denim work jacket, a light blue shirt with black leather bow tie and dark trousers stuffed into heavy work boots. His cap has a leather bill. He is brash, friendly and inquisitive.

ALF: He is the engine-driver. Alf is an older man, definitely the master of his locomotive. He is dressed like Bill; has a ruddy complexion which, like Bill's, has smudges. He sports a full, dark beard. He has a respect for his position. In addition, he is kind and rather sentimental.

WEASEL COOK: She is a plump lady weasel, middle-aged, and is dressed in gray, with a white cap and apron. She has a tendency to bawl her orders.

CHART OF STAGE POSITIONS

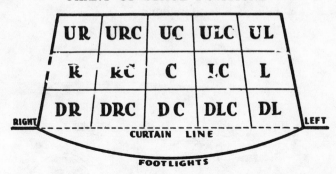

STAGE POSITIONS

Upstage means away from the footlights, *down-stage* means toward the footlights, and *right* and *left* are used with reference to the actor as he faces the audience. R means *right*, L means *left*, U means *up*, D means *down*, C means *center*, and these abbreviations are used in combination, as: U R for *up right*, R C for *right center*, D L C for *down left center*, etc. A territory designated on the stage refers to a general area, rather than to a given point.

NOTE: Before starting rehearsals, chalk off your stage or rehearsal space as indicated above in the *Chart of Stage Positions*. Then teach your actors the meanings and positions of these fundamental terms of stage movement by having them walk from one position to another until they are familiar with them. The use of these abbreviated terms in directing the play saves time, speeds up rehearsals, and reduces the amount of explanation the director has to give to his actors.

113

ACT ONE, SCENE TWO
Limousine

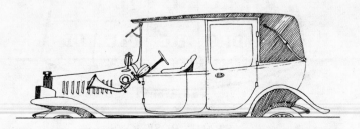

Limousine cut-out showing view from audience

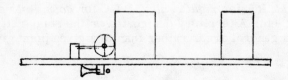

Top view of Limousine cut-out

114

Locomotive

Locomotive cut-out showing view from audience

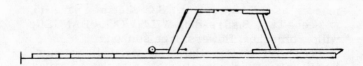

Top view of Locomotive cut-out

PROPERTIES

SET PIECES AND FURNITURE

ACT ONE:

Scene One: Small willow tree (optional); sign reading TOAD HALL / PRIVATE PROPERTY/KEEP OFF / THIS MEANS YOU!; pointer to WILD WOOD; few pieces of lawn furniture, including bench; wet handkerchief off R for Mole.

Scene Two: Two-dimensional cut-out set piece which represents the yellow limousine. (This is made of easily-cut composition board strengthened by light timber framing.) See sketch on page 114.

Scene Three: Area One: Flat containing barred cell door; crude table; two chairs or stools; rough cot; straw on floor. Area Two: Stool.

ACT TWO:

Scene One: Two-dimensional cut-out set piece which represents the locomotive (built in the same manner as the limousine). See sketch on page 115.

Scene Two: Sign reading WILD WOOD /DANGER; willow branches; flowers; tree stump.

Scene Three: Door flat; window flat; flat containing fireplace and mantel; table with three chairs; tea service for three on table.

Scene Four: Ladder covered with tarpaulin to give effect of ramp leading to tunnel; large basket or hamper containing weapons (belt, pistol and cutlass for each animal) and covered with a tarpaulin.

Scene Five: Two door flats with swinging doors; fireplace; chair; cutlass.

HAND PROPERTIES

ACT ONE, Scene One:

    MOLE: Handkerchief.
    RAT: Folded newspaper.
    BADGER: Walking stick, penny.
    TOAD: Steering wheel with horn-bulb, checkbook.
    JEN WEASEL: Bicycle.

ACT ONE, Scene Two:

    TOAD: Bicycle (same as used in Scene One), calling card, picture of Toad Hall, coin.
    POLICEMAN: Notebook and pencil.
    MOLE: Handkerchief.

ACT ONE, Scene Three:

    JAILER: Keys, plate of food.
    PENELOPE: Tray of hot buttered toast, tea and marmalade; pudding and punch; letter in apron pocket; basket containing washerwoman costume (cotton print gown, apron, shawl, bonnet), pillows and string, gag.
    MOLE: Bandage on head, sling on arm, paper and pen.

ACT TWO, Scene One:
    TOAD: Bundle of clothes, handkerchief.

ACT TWO, Scene Two:

    JACK: Short whip, jacket.
    PORTLY: Handful of flowers.

ACT TWO, Scene Three:

    MOLE: Cup of tea, biscuit.
    RAT: Five dark-lanterns.

ACT TWO, Scene Four:
    BADGER: Lantern, stick.

MOLE: Lantern, stick, washerwoman costume in sack.

MRS. OTTER: Broom, lantern.

RAT: Lantern, stick, handkerchief for gag.

TOAD: Lantern, stick.

ACT TWO, Scene Five:

PORTLY: Tray.

JACK WEASEL: Car horn.

TOAD: Stick, tablecloth.